Alice's Dad

the loss of a parent after a long illness

Bill Merrington

Illustrated by Lisa Russen

First published in 1999 by
KEVIN MAYHEW LTD
Buxhall
Stowmarket
Suffolk IP14 3DJ

Also by Bill Merrington
Suffering Love obtainable from Advantage, High Croft,
Cowgill Road, Dent, nr Sedbergh LA10 5TF
The Hideaway, published by Kevin Mayhew

0 1 2 3 4 5 6 7 8 9

ISBN 1 84003 374 6
Catalogue No 1500274

Cover illustration by Lisa Russen
Cover designed by Jaquetta Sergeant
Typesetting by Richard Weaver
Edited by Michael Forster
Printed and bound in Great Britain

Contents

STORY

Introduction   5
Chapter 1 A Flash of Memories   7
Chapter 2 Remembering Great Days   11
Chapter 3 A Strange Smell   15
Chapter 4 Losing Weight   21
Chapter 5 Never the Same   27
Chapter 6 Friction   33
Chapter 7 A Helping Hand   39
Chapter 8 So Many Questions   45
Chapter 9 Moving On   49

NOTES

Introduction   57
Notes on Chapter 1   59
Notes on Chapter 2   61
Notes on Chapter 3   63
Notes on Chapter 4   65
Notes on Chapter 5   69
Notes on Chapter 6   75
Notes on Chapter 7   83
Notes on Chapters 8 and 9   87

Special Notes on Murder   89
Special Notes on Suicide   91

To Jane

Introduction

As a young child I lived in a cul-de-sac where our house overlooked the school at the end of the street. Each day I heard the school bell and could see children going through the gate. For weeks and months I knew one day I too would attend this primary school. But when the 4th of September came I was not ready. I recall tearing a button off my new school shirt and having a crying fit. Why should I have to go to school when I had a safe home to play in, with my dog called Kim and my toys? But to school I went.

In the early days I remember standing in the school playground by the gate looking at my house. It was only 50 metres away, so close yet so far. There was a longing to escape and go home but each time the school bell sounded and drew me back to the classroom. I recall one day hurting my finger and ending up sitting on the teacher's knee, crying. I can remember her name, she was not mum or home, but she helped me cope and adapt to my new life.

We all experience times of change as children and adults. It could be moving house or school, or as in the following story, the loss of a special person like a mum or dad. How do we cope with such change especially when we wish it hadn't happened?

In *Alice's Dad*, we hear how one girl reacts when she finds out her dad is ill. The journey of seeing her dad die was difficult. How would she cope without him? Whose fault was it? How does it affect her other relationships? Where is Dad now? Will life ever be the same again? With the help of others she is able to work through her needs and problems. Despite the scar of her loss, she begins to find new hope and purpose for her life.

Alice's Dad is written for anyone, young or old, who is grappling with death and bereavement. For those experiencing loss, the book will enable them to see themselves within the story and, I hope, find tools to aid their recovery and growth. The story and notes on each chapter provide an opportunity for people to look at their own emotions and feelings towards the deceased and those around them. There is also encouragement to think about spiritual questions and to begin to find answers which give us hope and purpose for our lives.

Teachers in schools and churches will find the book a useful aid in encouraging young people to discuss their understanding of death and grief. The story will enable young people to reflect upon how they react with their emotions and feelings, as well as looking at Christian spiritual issues such as heaven and life after death. This book may also be used alongside another book called *The Hideaway*, which deals with the sudden death of a mother and how it affects a young boy at school.

I meet many adults today who seek to protect children from thinking about death and bereavement. From my experience and learning, however, I am convinced we must not pass on our fears to the younger generation, but rather be willing and able to share and discuss life and death issues fully with them. I hope *Alice's Dad* proves to be a tool in aiding this discussion. Finally, if you find yourself in some way identifying with Alice or her mum in this story, may I encourage you to share your feelings and experience with someone you trust. I do not know your story or how you feel but I do know, from listening to many people, that sharing your experience can help you to find growth points in your life.

BILL MERRINGTON

Chapter 1

A Flash of Memories

It was a bright, sunny afternoon in March as Alice sat on a park bench with her mum. It was easy to think she was in a park with trees all around the grassed area. In between the trees were scores and scores of daffodils pushing up through the layers of old autumn leaves. But there were no swings or children playing on the grass. It was a quiet, peaceful place. Behind Alice and her mum was a large hexagonal building. This was the only real clue to where they were sitting.

The local crematorium had been set in the beautiful surroundings of an old wood, not far from Alice's home town. It was the fifth anniversary since her dad had died. Each year Alice and her mum had come to the crematorium. They would bring a bunch of flowers and leave them in the wooded area where they had buried her dad's ashes.

'Do you want to come and see the book of remembrance?' asked Mum.

'Not just yet, Mum, I like sitting here.'

Alice's mum got up to head to the chapel where her husband's name was entered into the book of remembrance. 'Look, you can see your flowers from here; the reds of the tulips stand out among the yellow daffodils.' Alice did not reply – in fact she did not hear her mum. Her mind had meandered back in time. It was as if she was flicking through someone's diary of events. She felt she was an observer of the thoughts and pictures she was experiencing, and yet she knew they were a part of her own history. Mum by now had slowly walked to the chapel as tears welled up in Alice's eyes. She could have stopped the tears as she had done many times before. But somehow she felt it was good to let them flow.

Each tear seemed to bring to mind flashing pictures of the past. They were so vivid and clear. She could see her school . . . her friends . . . the street where she lived . . . her bedroom . . . Mum . . . Dad. In fact her earliest memory was of herself playing on the lounge carpet with her dad.

Alice loved her dad. It was not that she did not like her mum or grandparents, it was just that somehow Dad was special to her. Dad loved playing games. Together they would pretend to be cars or planes or submarines. Alice would sit on Dad's knee as he made the noises of helicopters and police cars. Being a submarine was Alice's favourite. Dad would make fish shapes with his hands such as an octopus, swordfish or flatfish while Alice steered the submarine up to the surface where suddenly they would become a police motor bike and rush through the streets of their town.

Each night, Mum would bath Alice before bedtime. Sometimes if Dad was free from work he would come up and join them. Dad would make up fairy stories of little people living amongst the vegetables in their garden. But best of all, Alice loved to sit on Dad's lap for her bedtime story. As Dad read *Postman Pat* or *Fireman Sam*, Alice loved to play with the hairs on the back of Dad's hand. She would brush them one way and make the hairs stand upright and then smooth them down again. She giggled as she finished with a little pull of his hairs which made Dad jump and look crossly at Alice. But she knew he was not really angry and seconds later they would be laughing again.

Mum and Dad always put Alice to bed together as she snuggled under her quilt. Mum and Dad would say a little prayer with Alice and give her a goodnight kiss on her forehead. Alice would quickly rub the kiss away with her hand as if she did not like it. But if Mum or Dad forgot she would shout out, 'You've forgotten my kiss!'

In the dark, alone, Alice was happy and content as she sucked her sheet and held her favourite toy, a furry white rabbit. She would quickly fall asleep knowing that Mum and Dad would be there in the morning.

Alice still had her white rabbit although it was a little worn by now. As she looked to the wooded area, Alice wondered where the real rabbits would be. She got up and moved towards the trees trying not to stand on the mole hills. 'It's strange,' she thought, 'you never see a mole hill being made but suddenly there they are.' It reminded her of the first time she ever realised there was a problem at home. It all seemed so long ago now.

Chapter 2

Remembering Great Days

When Alice was seven years old, she started to go to a new school. She soon made friends and enjoyed her new class teacher. Each day was much the same. Mum would collect Alice and they would walk home together. Alice often asked Mum to take her to the sweet shop but Mum always said that that was Dad's job at the weekend. Once through the front door, Alice would drop her lunch box and dash to put the TV on and collapse into her favourite chair. 'Drink of orange and a biscuit, please Mum,' she would shout. Mum would oblige with a grin on her face. Dad would get home from work at about 5.30 pm. Alice would hear the door open, and loved to run into Dad's arms for him to swing her around. To Alice, Dad was a giant. In fact he was so big he even made Mum look small.

But one day Alice came home to find Dad was already back from work. 'Why is Dad's car parked outside?' she asked.

'Your Dad's not well today,' explained her mum. 'He's in bed, so we'll have to be quiet.' But Alice rushed up stairs to see him.

'You don't look ill, Dad. Where's your spots?' Alice said in a loud voice.

Dad quietly explained, 'I'm ill inside, Alice. You can't see it but I have a dull ache here.' Dad pointed to his stomach. 'Now off you go and play like a good girl.' But Alice was full of energy. She started bouncing up and down on the bed. 'Alice,' Dad shouted, 'go downstairs!' Alice's eyes opened wide as she stared at Dad. It was rare for him to raise his voice and she was not used to it. She climbed off the bed and went downstairs, stamping her feet in anger.

It was quiet over tea time, with Mum and Alice eating downstairs and Dad still in bed. Usually each tea time the family would hold hands and say a prayer called a grace. This was a simple prayer of thanks for the food they were going to eat. Alice looked at Mum and asked, 'Mum, should we ask God to make Dad better?'

'Let's do that,' said Mum, 'because the doctor said that your Dad's going to be ill for a few weeks.'

Alice held hands with Mum and said simply, 'God, please make Dad better – and thank you for this food. Amen.'

After tea, Alice quickly forgot about Dad upstairs as a new friend in the house next door came to play. Days went by and Dad was still not feeling well. Some days, knowing that Dad was at home, Alice would not want to go to school. Mum could always tell. First Alice would not get out of bed when called. Then she would come downstairs in her pyjamas rather than get dressed. 'Oh Alice, go and get dressed, there is nothing wrong with you.'

'There is – I don't feel well,' Alice would shout.

Mum would grab her by the hand, 'Come along,' and make her put on her school uniform. It was not easy trying to fasten someone else's shirt especially when they were giggling, so Mum would often get cross. Alice would then cry and Mum would shout louder. 'Stand still will you, I can't do it with you moving – and stop crying, or you'll wake your dad up.' This made Alice furious, as Mum was now making more noise than she was! So, reluctantly, Alice went to school. Occasionally, however, Mum would give in and let her have a day off school .

Because of Dad's illness, keeping him off work, the family did not have a lot of money to buy extras at home. But when Dad had a day when he was feeling better, he would give Alice fifty pence to go and get some sweets at the corner shop at the end of the street. The man at the sweet shop knew Alice and her friend Suzy well. 'How's your dad, Alice?' he would ask.

Alice always replied, 'He's getting better,' as she and her friend rushed out and back to the house.

Eventually Dad began to get better. He would spend less time in bed and more time playing and reading to Alice. When Dad finally went back to work, Alice began to forget all about his illness.

The family soon got back into a new routine. The high-light for Alice was Saturday when Dad took her swim-ming. Dad would sit up in the balcony and read his newspaper. Knowing Dad was there, Alice would relax and enjoy her lesson. Now and again they would both look at each other at the same time and give each other a wave. There seemed to be a rapport between the two of them that made them very close to each other. On the way out Alice would always ask, 'Dad, have you got sixty pence today?'

Dad knew she wanted a can of drink from the machine. She would then stand for what seemed ages trying to decide what flavour to have. 'Come on, Alice, stick your money in and decide – there will soon be a queue!'

Now, in the crematorium grounds, Alice laughed to her-self, remembering how Mum also always said the same thing when they got home. 'Look at you both!' she would say, for Alice was still dripping wet and Dad was as red as beetroot because of the heat in the swimming centre.

'They were great days,' Alice whispered to herself, looking back.

By now she had walked to the edge of the grassed area, managing to keep her shoes clean of the newly thrown up earth. Alice decided to walk further into the wooded area. It was such a contrast from the mown lawn with its mole bumps. Alice could see how the wild area seemed to surround the tamed lawn. It looked as if the trees and shrubs were menacingly wanting to invade and take over the park-like area. Alice could identify with the feeling. 'One minute you're all excited and then "Bang!" you're up against it.'

Chapter 3

A Strange Smell

Three years after Dad's first illness, Alice was really looking forward to her birthday which was just a week before
Christmas. But it was only October, so there was still a
long wait ahead of her. One morning, Alice wondered
why Dad had not gone to work. She felt a knot in her
stomach that she had not experienced for a long time. She
hesitantly asked her mum, 'Why is Dad still in bed?'

Mum seemed reluctant in replying, 'Oh, he's going to
the doctor's, Alice. Your dad's not feeling well, but
there's nothing to worry about.'

Alice would always remember how those last few words
kept going around and around her head . . . 'Nothing to
worry about . . . nothing to worry about'. Alice could
always tell when Mum was hiding something: she would
speak quickly and sharply and not want to continue with
the conversation.

Alice's dad began to have more time in bed over the
following days. One Tuesday, Mum told Alice she was
going to be off school for the day. 'Your dad's got to go
into hospital for some tests for two days, Alice, so it's
easier if you stay at home and visit the hospital with me
in the afternoon.'

Alice pulled a strange face at Mum. 'What's wrong,
Alice?' asked Mum.

'Is Dad's test like the one I get at school?' replied Alice.

Mum laughed, 'No, the doctors just want to find out why your dad's still ill. They are going to put a tube down into his stomach to see if anything is wrong.'

'Ugh, I wouldn't like that,' replied Alice as she went off to watch television.

It was the first time Alice had ever been into a hospital. 'Have I ever been here before?' she asked Mum on the bus.

'Only when you were born,' said Mum.

'I don't remember that. Will I be able to see where I was born?'

'No,' said Mum. 'Dad's in a different ward from mummies and babies. He's in a room where there are just men.'

Alice was amazed at how long the corridors were, and surprised to see a bedroom with ten beds in. Dad explained, 'There are too many people needing hospital help to give everyone a room of their own. So they put people together so that nurses and doctors can look after everyone. It's a hospital ward, not a bedroom.' Alice was very quiet in the hospital – it was all so different. There were people in uniforms rushing around, and Alice felt that everything they said to each other could be heard by all the other patients in the ward. But most of all Alice did not like the smell of the hospital. Somehow it smelt different from home or school.

As Alice ate some of Dad's grapes, the man in the next bed asked, 'Is this your daughter then?'

'Yes,' said Dad, 'this is Alice. She'll soon be ten years old.' Alice blushed bright red, because she hated anyone talking about her. She pulled at Mum's skirt,

'What's wrong, Alice?'

Alice pointed at the curtain. 'What's this for?'

'You can pull it around the bed if you want to talk quietly or if the nurse comes to see the patient.'

Alice started pulling the curtain around as Dad began to explain to Mum about the tests. 'You would have liked this machine: one minute I was standing up drinking some white milky stuff, and then the machine picked me up and laid me down and I could see the inside of my stomach on a television screen.'

'*Was* it milk?'

' No, it's called a Barium meal – it was not very tasty, more like milky chalk.'

'Yuk!' Alice pulled a face, 'I wouldn't like that! Are you better now, Dad, can you come home?'

'I'm coming home tomorrow, but I won't know if I'm better for a little while yet.'

Alice was surprised how much she could remember of those days. She could picture vividly Mum and Dad staring at each other. She could recall the day Dad came home. She had been so pleased, but could remember how her parents argued that night. Alice felt it had been all her fault. She kept going on and on at Dad that she wanted a computer for Christmas. 'It can be my birthday present as well.'

Dad kept saying 'We'll see, we'll see,' and Mum told her to stop going on about Christmas. But it was when Alice was in bed that she heard them arguing. She couldn't make out what the argument was about, but felt it was somehow her fault. It was a long time afterwards that she realised that they were arguing about the computer.

'How on earth are we going to get a computer? You tell me. We've hardly had any money coming in since you've been ill!'

'I know, I know.'

The noise echoed throughout the house. Alice never saw or heard her mum and dad make up and be friends but she guessed they must have done because the next day it was as if it had not occurred. All Alice knew was that she got her computer. It proved to the best Christmas she could recall. Dad quietly read the manual and together they learned how to use it. Mum was not keen, though. Whenever Alice tried to get Mum to play a game, Mum would make an excuse and say she was busy. So the computer became something special that Dad and Alice had in common. It was like the old days before Dad was ill.

Alice brought her thoughts back to the present time, and bent down to pick a wild flower. It was one of the last snowdrops with its delicate drooping head. She put it to her nose to smell but it seemed to have no fragrance. Alice continued walking through the wooded area, trying to avoid standing on the wild flowers while she held onto her snowdrop. It was much harder to walk through the wood than she thought. There were no paths, just tree after tree, but she kept going till she could not see the crematorium building and its lawns any more. 'Why isn't there a path!' she exclaimed.

Chapter 4

Losing Weight

After that Christmas, Dad had begun to spend more time in bed. He ate less and became thinner. Alice would still see him each day but mainly in the bedroom. On good days Dad taught Alice how to play draughts and they would race each other with cars on the computer. A few times Dad was well enough to take Alice swimming and watch from the balcony. Alice enjoyed looking up and seeing Dad give her a wave. It was easy to believe he was well again when he was at the swimming pool, but it did not last long.

Alice's mum often told her to play in the lounge and not in the bedroom. Doctors and nurses would visit Dad and Alice would notice unusual smells after they had visited.

'What is that smell, Mum?'

'It's just the medicine and cleaning soap the nurse uses to help your dad to get washed,' explained Mum.

Alice did not like the doctor and nurses because she felt they saw Dad more than she did. 'Dad's worse since they visited,' she complained one day. Mum got cross and told her that the doctor and nurses were only trying to help Dad.

Alice's mum seemed to get annoyed with her more often since Dad was ill. She seemed to be constantly telling Alice to play quietly. Alice would go to her bedroom and wonder if it was her fault that Dad was ill. She played with her toys and dolls and made up games where her doll was ill and she was the nurse. She would scold her doll and tell her she should be getting better.

During this time, Neil, the curate from the local church started to visit Dad. They seemed to chat for ages and Alice wished he would leave so she could spend time with Dad. But Neil loved draughts, so he and Alice would often have a game before he left. 'You know your dad's very ill, Alice, don't you?' he said quietly.

Alice did not reply. The curate continued by asking, 'Do you think your dad's getting better or worse?' Alice suddenly felt angry with Neil's question and threw her draughtsman onto the board and stormed upstairs to her bedroom.

Lying on her bed she talked to her white rabbit. 'It's all his fault. I prayed to his God but he's making Dad worse.' Tears welled up in her eyes as she plucked at the fur on her rabbit.

One day Alice came home from school to find Dad's bed had been moved to another bedroom by himself. There was a large gas cylinder by the bed with a face mask. 'What's that for?' asked Alice as she pointed to the cylinder.

'It's to help me to breathe, Alice,' said Dad.

Alice could see Dad was in pain as he adjusted his position in the bed. 'Can you help me move my pillow?' he asked.

'Why is your skin so baggy, Dad?'

'It's because I've lost weight.'

Alice suddenly found herself asking, 'Are you going to die, Dad?'

Dad tapped the bed and said, 'Come and sit here beside me.' Dad spoke in a quiet voice these days; Alice could see as he spoke that he was struggling to swallow. 'You know I've not been well for some time. I don't know if I'm going to die, Alice, but I love you. And if I do die then I know you'll help Mum, won't you?'

Alice didn't speak but she gently nodded her head.

'If I die,' said Dad, 'I'll go to heaven, so I'll be all right, won't I?'

Alice was just about to ask Dad what heaven was like when Mum came in and told her in a stern voice to give her dad a rest and not to upset him. 'I didn't!' cried Alice, and dashed out to her bedroom.

'I find it very hard when you talk like that,' Mum complained.

23

'So do I,' replied her husband, 'but we must prepare Alice for the future. Try not to take out your anger on Alice, it's not her fault.'

Mum gave her husband a gentle cuddle as she whispered, 'I know, I'm just worried that I'm not going to cope. It's all just too much. We have debts, I'll have to sell the car, the computer – and how will Alice react?' There was a long silence between them.

Over the next few weeks, lots of relatives and friends seemed to call at the house to see Dad. Alice didn't want to go to school but her mum made her attend. One day at the end of school time Alice saw her mum coming out of the head teacher's office. It looked as if Mum had been crying. 'What's wrong, Mum?' asked Alice, but she just said nothing.

Alice and her mum could see that Dad was getting weaker and weaker. He looked thin in the face and slept a lot of the time. Mum seemed to want Alice to spend more time at her friend's house after school. She would often stay for tea and not get back home until seven o'clock. Alice enjoyed playing with her friend, but as soon as she got home a feeling of anger would well up within her. Why could things not get back to normal? Mum would snap at her, 'Oh stop being moody!' But Alice would ignore her by switching on the computer and playing 'Lemmings'. She would take out her frustration by blowing up the lemmings. This only annoyed Mum further – she didn't understand the computer, and hated the noise of the games. However, Mum did let her daughter play – and stay up later and later each night. As the days progressed Mum became increasingly tired. In the past her hair had always been washed, combed and held into place by hair spray. Now it had grown long and straggly. Alice began to wonder if Mum was ill, like Dad.

As Alice grappled with these memories of the past, she could feel herself getting more and more annoyed with each step she took through the wood near the cemetery. Her shoes had become caked in mud and it was becoming increasingly hard for her to go on. She decided to look around for somewhere to sit. A pine tree had been totally uprooted by the wind and was lying trapped between its neighbouring trees. Alice managed to lift herself up through the branches to sit on the trunk. She wanted just to sit quietly and swing her legs as if she were five years old again, but the thoughts kept coming. Away from the sun in the shade of the wood, she felt a breeze that made her nerves twitch and her arms shake. She knew she was going to think about the day she had blanked out in her mind. She tried to block the thoughts – to push them back down into her mind where they had been locked away for so long. But it was as if the breeze were blowing open her treasure chest of memories. 'I don't want to think about it, I don't!' she said out loud. Tears ran down into her mouth. She could taste the salt. Somehow the taste of the tears calmed Alice. It seemed to give her strength to face her thoughts – to face herself.

Chapter 5

Never the Same

One day Alice had come home from school to find the doctor and the nurse in the house. Alice could see Mum had been crying, and that made her want to go upstairs to see Dad, but Mum said, 'Not just now, Alice.' So Alice went into the lounge to watch television.

The doctor came into the room and her mum came and switched the television off. The doctor sat down on the settee by Alice and said, 'Alice, I'm sorry but your dad has died'. He told her that her dad was now free of any pain.

'Where is he?' Alice asked. 'Is he in heaven?'

'His body is still upstairs in the bedroom. Would you like to go up and see him?' said the doctor.

Alice was not sure what to do but the doctor encouraged her to go and see her dad. When she went into the bedroom it looked as if Dad were asleep, but he did not move and he looked very pale and thin. The nurse helped Alice to touch and hold her dad's hand. Alice felt the hand that she loved to stroke which was now cold to touch. She bent down and kissed the hand, and then went downstairs and switched on the computer.

'Are you all right, Alice?' Mum asked her.

Alice answered, 'The computer's mine now,' and after a long pause added, 'have you been crying?'

'Yes' said Mum, 'do *you* feel like crying?'

Alice just shook her head and continued playing on the computer. That night, several people came to the house including the curate. They all said how sorry they were to Alice and her mum.

'Have I two dads now?' asked Alice, 'One in heaven and one upstairs?'

The curate talked to Alice about how the special part of her dad went to heaven where he would get a new body. The three of them then went upstairs and the curate prayed for Alice's dad and asked God to help Alice and her mum in the coming days. Later that evening, two men came, and while Alice and her mum stayed in the lounge they took her dad to a special room in a large house called a chapel of rest.

It was a strange evening. Neither Mum nor daughter knew what to do with herself. Alice went on and off the computer. The television played all night but no one really watched it, and Mum seemed to make lots of drinks, most of which she wasted.

'It's getting late, Alice, you ought to be in bed.'

Alice did not reply.

'Alice!' said her mum, loudly.

Alice wanted to say, 'Be quiet, Dad's sleeping,' but she stopped the words coming out of her mouth. 'I can't,' she sobbed, 'I don't like going up there alone.'

Mum let out a big sigh. 'You can sleep in my bed tonight, come on.'

In the safety of Mum's bed, Alice did sleep but she sensed that Mum was awake all night.

Alice had the next day off school. The curate came again and talked to Alice about her dad. They remembered how he liked music and reading books. 'He taught me how to play draughts,' said Alice. 'I can sometimes beat him!'

At times it would seem as if Dad were still in his bedroom and Alice would play like normal. But at other moments Alice would want to go and sit with Mum to feel safe and secure. The nurse came and took the medical equipment and medicines away. Alice did not know whether she was pleased or sad to have the medical smell leave the house. Dad's bedroom looked bare and cold. Mum kept the door closed.

The night before the funeral, Alice stayed at home with her auntie while her mum went to the chapel of rest to see Dad. Alice wondered what it would be like but she didn't really want to go.

Hearing the footsteps of someone walking up the path outside the house, Alice dashed to the door to see if it was Mum. It wasn't, but Auntie assured her that she would soon be back. When the door did open, Alice ran to her mum for a cuddle, but Mum was exhausted: 'Give me some space, Alice, please.'

Alice did not know what to do. She would normally run upstairs to cuddle her rabbit but she felt frightened now. So she went and hid behind the sofa.

'How was it?' asked Auntie. Alice could picture Mum putting her finger to her lips and mouthing, 'Shh, I'll tell you later.' But Alice wanted to know now. It all seemed unfair to Alice. She felt only her dad would have understood her feelings.

At first, Alice was not going to go to the funeral. Her auntie thought she should stay with her in the house but the curate wanted Alice to attend. Alice felt numb about any decision, so her mum decided she should go with her to the funeral but not to the crematorium. As they drove in the funeral car, no one spoke. All of Dad's relatives and friends had filled the church as Alice and her mum walked in behind the coffin. Everyone stood as the curate read out verses from the Bible.

'Jesus said, "I am the resurrection, and I am the life; he who believes in me, though he die, yet shall he live, and whoever lives and believes in me shall never die".'

It was strange to be sitting so close to the coffin, thought Alice, while the curate was speaking about her dad as if he were alive. Alice fidgeted on the wooden pew and kicked the prayer kneeler in front of her. The curate talked about the life of her dad, where he was born and what he did as a young person. The curate seemed to know things about Dad that even Alice didn't know. At the end, the curate said how special Alice had been to Dad and how important it was to remember all the good times they had had together. As they sat during the prayers, Alice looked across at the coffin. It seemed much longer than her dad. On the top was a wreath of flowers with a card saying, 'Love from June and Alice'.

When everyone sung the second hymn, Alice's mum began to cry and cry. Alice reached out a hand and together they cuddled each other. Four big men carried the coffin out of the church. Alice watched the hearse drive away to the crematorium as she walked home with her auntie. She felt all confused inside. She really wanted to be with Mum yet she equally did not want to go to the crematorium.

After the funeral lots of people came to the house. It was like a party with food and drink. As Alice helped handing out food she found herself being giggly – so much so that Mum got cross. Alice ran to her bedroom and dived onto her bed and cried. It was the first time she had cried since her dad had died. Mum went into Alice's bedroom and tried to cuddle her daughter. At first Alice resisted but she finally gave in. 'It's good to cry, Alice,' said her mum. They sat on together cuddling and crying. It felt good to be warm with Mum.

'Mum! she'll be wondering where I am,' thought Alice, wrenching her thoughts back to the present. It felt as if she had been alone in the wood for ages but her watch showed that only minutes had passed by. Alice searched in her pocket for a hanky as she sniffed and sniffed. She felt she could have sat there for ever. 'Life's simpler by yourself. No one to worry about or to annoy you.'

At that moment, Alice heard a noise that made her jump. She never saw whether it had been a rabbit or a mole or something else, but it was enough to stop her wandering in her thoughts. She needed to get back to Mum, but she remained sitting still. 'Just a minute more,' she thought, 'then I'll go back.'

Chapter 6

Friction

In the days that followed there was a big gap in Alice's life. She missed Dad. 'Why don't you go and play with your friend?' her mum suggested. Alice didn't reply. 'Oh go on, Alice – play on the computer or read a book, but do something!' Alice looked at Mum with real anger in her eyes, but she still didn't say anything. She simply went upstairs to her room. She coped now with going upstairs by herself – provided Dad's door was closed.

In the silence downstairs, Mum had much to worry about. Without Dad's wage coming in, Mum knew she had to make some serious cut-backs in spending. She wanted to get rid of the computer but she knew how much it meant to her daughter. Eventually she would have to get a job and hope it fitted in with Alice's school times. But upstairs, Alice had her own worries and was unaware of the pressures on her mum.

As the days passed, Alice had more and more days off school. One day it was a tummy ache, another day it was a headache. At first, Mum was determined to get Alice to school, but Mum herself had lost her drive and energy. So she stopped forcing Alice to go. They would spend the day at home getting under each other's feet. One day it reached a point where neither of them could cope. 'Look,' said Mum, 'it's a sunny day – go and get some fresh air.'

'Why should I?' replied Alice. 'You never go out.'

'Don't get cheeky with me,' said Mum.

'Well there's nothing else to do, is there?' shouted Alice. 'Dad would take me swimming or to the sweet shop, but you don't do anything with me. You can't even play draughts!'

'How dare you!' exclaimed Mum.

'It's true – you got rid of Dad and now you want rid of me!'

Mum was silent, stunned by what Alice had said, and sat down on the settee in a daze. It wasn't true, she thought, but she realised how little she had been doing with Alice.

Alice realised she had said more than she had really wanted to. 'I'm sorry, Mum – I didn't really mean it.' She sat next to Mum and they gave each other a hug.

'I'm sorry, too. I spend so much time thinking about your dad. I just haven't any energy these days to do anything.'

'It's okay, Mum,' said Alice.

'You don't really think I got rid of Dad, do you?'

Alice was silent for a moment, before she asked, 'Why did Dad move out of your bedroom?'

'Your dad was so ill, love, he needed as much rest as possible. I was disturbing him, so the doctor suggested he would be better in a different room, that's all.'

They were both quiet, and it seemed to last for hours before Mum broke the silence.

'You know your dad would have really wanted you to be still going to school.'

Alice didn't reply at first, although she knew it was true. 'Do you think Dad knows?' she eventually asked.

'I don't know, Alice, I just don't know,' replied Mum.

'The curate would know, wouldn't he?'

'Perhaps.' Mum stroked Alice's long hair, and began to wonder whether she ought to talk to someone about Alice and herself. But it was hard to admit they needed help.

The following Sunday, Mum and Alice went to the early morning service at the local church. It was only around the corner. Together they held hands as they went into church as it was their first time in the building since the funeral. The service was a Holy Communion which lasted for about one hour. Mum was unsure whether they could receive the bread and wine, so they left early, hoping no one noticed them leave. Two days later, the curate came to Alice's house. Mum was surprised at first to see Neil, but after making him a cup of tea she felt a little more relaxed.

'I was doing the school assembly the other day and noticed that Alice was missing – how is she?' he asked.

'She's fine,' Mum replied, unsure what to say. 'We went to church last Sunday.'

'Yes, the vicar said he saw you. I'm sorry I wasn't there, but I was doing the later service. Perhaps you and Alice would prefer that one – it's a family service with lively music and lots of other children present.'

'Oh, no, I couldn't cope with lots of people – and the singing would only make me cry.' Mum's voice dropped almost to a whisper. 'Anyway, we're not a family any more, are we?'

'Yes you are,' answered Neil. 'I'm sure your husband would want you both still to be a family.'

'It's easy for him, he doesn't have to cope with a moody daughter – Alice is missing him terribly.'

There was a long silence. 'What about you – have you anyone to talk to?' asked Neil.

Alice's mum sounded surprised. 'What about?'

'People often find it helps,' explained Neil, 'if they have someone to share their thoughts and feelings about their loved one with and how they are coping now.'

'Oh!' she said. 'I think Alice would find that helpful.'

'Why don't you ask the doctor? I know they have a bereavement counsellor who would come and support you both.'

Before the curate left, he asked to see Alice and they had an enjoyable game of draughts. 'I have a computer disk of games I don't use any more, and I think it has draughts on it. I'll bring it for you next time and you can see if you can beat the computer.' Alice liked Neil, and his visit encouraged Mum to go to the doctor and to arrange for a counsellor to visit them both.

Still sitting in the woods, Alice looked down again at her

shoes. What a mess! She broke off a twig from a branch of the dead tree and started to poke the clay clinging to her heels. She tried to do it while still keeping her hands clean, but the stick kept breaking. Alice rarely cleaned shoes. She relied upon Mum to do such things for her. She thought of how much she needed her. There were so many things Mum had done for Alice. Yes, there had been a time when Mum could do nothing right for her, but they had grown much closer since then, especially with the help of others.

Chapter 7

A Helping Hand

When Anne, the counsellor, called, Alice was unsure whether she wanted to see her so she stayed upstairs at first and listened from the landing. As soon as she heard Anne say, 'I bumped into the curate on the pavement outside, and he gave me this CD for Alice,' Alice shot down the steps and into the lounge.

'Hello,' Anne greeted her, with a big smile. 'You must be Alice?'

'Yes – can you put the disk into my computer?'

'Well, I'll try,' said Anne.

Mum left the two of them to the computer and went and waited nervously in the kitchen.

One hour later the three of them had agreed that Anne would come every two weeks to see Alice and if Alice wanted to share with her mum any of the things they said or did, then she could.

Every time Anne came to see Alice, they would finish by playing draughts on the computer. 'Look, Mum,' said Alice, after the second visit, 'Anne got me to draw four pictures of spring, summer, autumn and winter.'

'That's nice,' said Mum, 'you seem to get on well with Anne.'

'Yes, but we just chat, you know. She's given me some homework.'

'Really – what is it?'

'She wants me to think of four things I liked doing with Dad and to draw them in this booklet with pictures of the seasons.'

'Wow! What do you think you will draw?' asked Mum.

'I don't know.' Alice was already dashing out to see her friend who lived next door.

At their next meeting, Alice told Anne how interested Mum was in her booklet. Anne asked Alice if she'd mind if Mum filled in one too.

'Great,' said Alice. She rushed into the kitchen. 'Mum, Mum, Anne says you can do some drawing too. Come and join us.'

'I can't draw,' said Mum, hesitantly.

However, by Anne's third visit Alice and her mum were working through their booklets at their own pace. Anne mainly saw Alice by herself, but on some occasions Mum joined in.

Alice and her mum had fun finding old photographs of each other to show Anne how much they had changed over their lives. Anne asked them to find photographs of Dad, too, when he was at different ages. This was much harder, and when Mum and her daughter looked at the last photo taken of Dad all three held each other and had a good cry. The exercise Alice enjoyed most was making a jar of different coloured salts. Each colour was to represent some special memory of Dad. When they were finished, Mum and Alice placed them on each side of the mantel-piece. Alice had chosen bright blue to represent the times Dad took her to the swimming baths, and yellow was the time when they went to the beach at the seaside. She made the yellow gradually become dark purple to show the time that Dad was ill.

Mum had chosen two streaks of brown to be the times when her husband had become ill. For her, the first illness was the worst because it was the time that she and Dad had really kept his illness to themselves.

Anne helped Alice to draw a picture of the sea, with big waves. She showed Alice how to see that her feelings were just like the waves: sometimes everything feels okay and good. 'This is just like the sea when it's calm and beautiful and restful,' said Anne.

'I'm like that – the worst times are when I wake up, or at night when I don't want to go to bed.'

'That's like the sea when it's high and frothy and full of energy and is rushing into the bay to knock you over,' explained Anne. 'But you know that the sea comes and goes, and your feelings will be just the same. What do you think about in bed, Alice?'

Alice did not answer but had her own question, 'Will I ever forget Dad?'

'Are you worried that you might, then?'

Alice nodded. 'It's why I can't get to sleep. Sometimes I think that in the morning Dad will be here, or I think I'll wake up and have no memories of him.'

Anne helped Alice to accept that her dad was dead, but also that her thoughts and memories were precious and no one could take them away from her.

Anne, Alice and her mum then played a game of cards. Each card had a face and a word explaining how the face felt – happy, sad, angry, and so on. When one of them picked up a card they had to tell of a time when they felt like that. Mum didn't find it easy to share with Alice about the times she felt angry or sad, but she eventually felt better for doing so.

The session finished with Anne asking the two of them to think of a place where they felt safe and secure. Alice said it was in bed with Mum and her white rabbit. Mum, however, found the question harder to answer and said she would think about it.

One day, Alice asked, 'Where is Dad?'

'I'll tell you what – why don't we ask Neil, the curate, to come next time? Perhaps he could help us.'

'Oh, good!' said Alice. 'He's wicked at draughts.'

Alice looked forward to Anne's visits, but there were many difficult days in between. And now, as Alice sat alone on the tree trunk in the crematorium grounds, she could feel the pain inside her as she recalled the day Mum sold the computer.

It all happened so suddenly. Alice could tell Mum was keeping a secret but she did not realise what it was until

42

the day she came home from school and saw the empty desk. At first, Alice did not say anything but looked around the lounge. Mum stayed in the kitchen, pretending to be busy.

'Where's my computer?' asked Alice, quietly.

'It's gone. I've sold it. We need the money.' said Mum sternly.

Alice exploded. 'It was my computer, mine. Dad gave it to me, not you. You had no right, I hate you, I hate you!'

Mum did not move or speak; she stood rooted to the floor, looking out of the window as if she had not heard. Alice banged the kitchen door and went to her friend's house. It took a lot of consoling and explaining by Alice's friend's mum before she calmed down. 'She loves you, Alice, but she's finding it tough, too, you know.' It was the first time Alice was struck with the thought that Mum missed Dad as much as she did. Until now it had looked as if Mum was not missing Dad at all, what with all her busyness. It took a few days before Mum and Alice could look at each other properly. From that time on, Alice decided she wanted to sleep back in her own bed. They both found it hard sleeping separately but neither of them admitted it.

Still in the crematorium grounds, Alice had by now given up cleaning her shoes. She jumped from the tree trunk and proceeded to head back to the park bench. She could see cars to the right of her. It was another cortège heading towards the crematorium. 'Another group of people mourning,' she thought. 'I wonder whether they'll be asking the same questions as I did.'

Just as she thought this, she tripped and ended up flat in the tall wild grasses. She was about to curse, when her eyes spotted a tiny movement ahead of her. Alice froze, trying to hold her breath. A young rabbit had frozen also at the noise of Alice's fall. In that split second it was as if Alice and the rabbit had seen eye to eye with each other and fully understood one another. A second later, the rabbit was gone, diving down into its burrow. It left Alice alone again, only this time her thoughts made her smile – thinking about a different kind of rabbit all together.

Chapter 8

So Many Questions

It was a few weeks later that Neil, the curate, came to see Alice again. She was busy swinging on the playground swings with her friend.

'I'll see you soon,' Alice said to her friend, as she jumped off the swing and ran to Neil. 'What have you got there,' she asked, pointing to Neil's hand.

'I've got a special book to read to you, and some writing paper and an envelope,' said Neil.

'What are we going to do?'

Neil laughed, 'Wait and see!'

Alice had another question for Neil as they walked to her front door. 'Why do you wear that earring in one ear?'

Neil was quick in answering, 'Why do you wear that bangle on your wrist?'

Alice did not answer, but it set her thinking.

When in the house with Mum, Neil explained to Alice that his own mum died several years ago. 'I was left a few of Mum's possessions, and she had one set of earrings that were plain enough for me to wear. So you see it's special. Do you have anything special that belonged to your dad?'

'I don't know really,' replied Alice. It gave Mum an idea for later on.

'Now, I know you have some questions for me,' said Neil, 'but I've written a list of questions *I* thought you might have:

Where is Dad now?

Does Dad know what I'm doing?

Will I see Dad again?

Why do I ache inside?

What's heaven like?

Will my mum get a new husband?

Why didn't Jesus stop Dad from dying?'

'There's a question you've missed,' said Alice.

'What is it?' enquired Neil.

Alice said her question – but she spoke so quietly, with her hand covering her mouth, that Neil could not hear.

'I'll go and make you a cup of tea, Neil,' said Mum.

After she had gone to the kitchen, Alice asked the question again. 'Will Mum die?'

'That's a good question, Alice, well done for asking it,' Neil congratulated her.

Neil tried the best he could to answer some of Alice's questions. 'Sometimes, Alice, when you play draughts you just don't know what to move next. But it's okay – you make your mind up and whether you win or not you've at least done your best. Some of these questions are like that. We don't know all the answers, but we try and make sense of them and just do our best in life and leave the rest to God who knows everything. Because he loves us, we can trust all the answers to him.'

'What's heaven like?' asked Alice.

'Well, I've not been there, but I know God who made earth also made heaven, and since heaven is perfect it must have all the best things from earth in it.'

'I wish I could speak to Dad,' said Alice.

'Wow! You've read my mind!' exclaimed Neil. 'I've brought an envelope and some writing paper – I thought we might write a letter to your dad.'

'But how are we going to get it to him?' laughed Alice.

'Well,' said Neil, 'you know God knows all things. I think if you want, I could take it to church and just pray that God reads it and looks after your dad. So shall we have a go?'

Alice did not find it easy to write a letter. There was so much she wanted to say but found it hard to think. Neil was trying to help her as Mum came in with the tea.

'Is there anything you want to ask Dad, Alice – perhaps something you've felt angry about?'

'I want to ask him why he left me – was it my fault?' Alice began to cry and Neil and her mum gave her a cuddle.

'You know, Alice, sometimes I felt angry at my mum

47

for dying, but I still loved her. No, it wasn't my fault, or your fault.'

Alice looked at Neil but said nothing. When he left, Neil suggested to Alice drawing a painting of heaven and she said she would try.

'What about your story book?' asked Alice.

'Oh, I nearly forgot. I'll leave it with you – it's the story of *The Velveteen Rabbit**. You read it with Mum, and tell me what you think about it.'

Remembering all this, Alice picked herself up from her thoughts and from the ground. She clutched a cross around her neck to see that it was safe. Back onto the grassed area, she could see that Mum had still not returned to the seat. The dirt on her shoes began to loosen and she found that she could walk more freely. She sat back down on the bench, suddenly aware that she had lost her snowdrop. Whenever she lost or mislaid anything, she would often find herself holding or fiddling with the gold cross. It was a comfort to her. 'It was a good day when I got this,' she thought.

The Velveteen Rabbit is a story of a boy who becomes ill. He cuddles his favourite toy, the rabbit. When he is better the boy gets a new present – a new stuffed toy. The rabbit is about to be thrown out but a fairy makes him real. She tells him that he has become real because the boy loved him so much. The boy never forgets the rabbit and at times thinks he sees it alive in the woods.

Chapter 9

Moving On

It was now a few months since Alice's dad had died. Her mum had not felt able to sort out his belongings, his clothes, books and jewellery. But after Neil's discussion with Alice, Mum decided she wanted to sort out a few special things of Dad's which she could give to Alice to keep as mementoes.

When Alice got home from school, she found a surprise waiting for her. 'What's this shoe box out for – have you bought me some new trainers?'

'Not quite,' said Mum, 'but I hope you'll look after the things I've put in the box for you.'

Alice's eyes widened to find several special things belonging to Dad. There was Dad's watch, a crucifix on a chain, a photograph of Dad and Alice on holiday, one of Dad's favourite books and two spare draughts pieces, one white and one black.

'Thanks, Mum,' said Alice, as she pressed the buttons on Dad's watch and made it bleep. Mum and Alice laughed as they tried to switch it off.

One suggestion that came out of Anne's and Neil's visits was for Mum to take Alice with Neil to the crematorium to show her where Dad went at the end of the funeral. It was a modern hexagonal building in the middle of a wooded area. Because it was early spring there were lots of daffodils growing wild between the trees.

Neil explained that when someone is cremated the coffin and body are burned in a very hot furnace.

'What's left are called the ashes. I've got your dad's here which we are going to scatter somewhere among the trees,' said Neil.

Alice felt strange and a little nervous. 'Would Dad have felt anything in the fire?'

'No,' explained Neil. 'A person is like a box of chocolates: what's important is the sweets and not the box. The sweets are the special part of your dad that has gone to be with God. But the sweet box is still special to us. Why don't you choose a special place for us to put the ashes?'

Alice chose a quiet spot in between the trees and the daffodils. Neil dug a little hole to put the ashes into the ground. Together the three of them held hands and said a special prayer.

Almost a year later, on the anniversary of Dad's death, the three of them met again with a spade, only this time it was outside the swimming baths on the edge of the park. It was Anne the counsellor's idea. She suggested that people find it helpful sometimes to plant a tree to remember a loved one. Mum decided the type of tree and Alice chose the location. Because Dad loved to take her swimming, Alice thought it would be nice to plant a tree that you could see from the swimming pool. Alice's mum asked Neil to get special permission from the council to plant the tree. It was another lovely day, with the sun shining but rather cold in the winter air. They planted the tree together and Neil said a prayer of thanks for Alice's dad and for how well Alice and her mum had supported each other. Afterwards, back at home, Anne joined them and they had tea together.

Alice went to show Neil her work booklet that she had completed with Anne. 'Mum's got one too,' said Alice.

'You've both done well,' replied Neil. 'It's like being on a journey since your dad's died. There have been good days and bad days but together you've come a long way since last year.'

'Mum's going to go to college to retrain as a cook,' said Alice, excitedly.

'Yes, and I'm terrified,' Mum admitted.

'That's understandable,' said Anne. 'You'll still have good and bad days ahead of you, but together you have learned to cope and adjust.'

'It's like the weather,' said Mum. 'Some days I get up and it's as if it's cloudy and I feel down and heavy. But at least I know it doesn't last. Another day and it's sunny again. We have to keep remembering for ourselves that we are okay, don't we, Alice?'

But Alice had dashed upstairs. 'I'm pleased you've got a job and are going to retrain,' said Neil.

'Yes, the hours are not too bad and Alice's friend's mum picks her up from school and looks after her 'til I'm back at five. It'll take me a while to sort out the finances, but when I do I'll buy her another computer.'

'I'm pleased,' said the curate.

Alice came back in, carrying the Velveteen Rabbit book. 'Thank you, I know the story off by heart, now.'

'So do I,' said Neil. 'It's lovely to think of the rabbit becoming more real because of the love of the boy.'

'And Dad will always be loved by us,' said Alice. 'It helps me to think he is whole again without being poorly.'

'And me,' said her mum, 'and me.'

The crematorium was busy, and Alice's thoughts were suddenly distracted by the noise of people getting out of cars. Another funeral was taking place. In those five years, Alice had met other people who had had relatives and friends die. She had been forced to grow up a lot in that time. When Mum had bought her another computer, she realised how hard Mum had been working to help her. Now the two of them were as much friends as mother and daughter. She still missed Dad of course, at the swimming baths, in the sweet shop, and at home. But the curate and Anne were right: her memories remained with her and became more and more precious as time went on.

Alice had not seen her mum drawing near.

'I've found your dad's name. Are you sure you don't want to see it?' asked Mum.

'Okay, let's go together.'

Alice and her mum walked arm in arm across the lawn. No one would have known, looking at them, what they both had experienced and come through.

'What on earth has happened to your shoes?' asked Mum.

Alice looked down and smiled. 'Quite a lot, Mum, quite a lot.' She squeezed Mum's arm and said cheekily, 'Don't worry – you're good at cleaning shoes – but I think this time I'll help you.'

NOTES

Introduction

Perhaps you read this book because someone you love has died, or perhaps you have a friend whose mum or dad has died and you want to know how you can help them. These notes explore different feelings people have when someone they love dies. Now that you have read about what happened to Alice, you might like to talk to a parent, grandparent, teacher or someone else you trust. You can show them the story and the notes and this will help you to face difficult questions together and share feelings about what has happened.

Notes on Chapter 1

A Flash of Memories

When someone you care for has died, you will find that a lot of your time is spent thinking about them. Do not worry about this for most people react in this way. However long ago or recently your loved one died, it can help to think through all that has happened to you. Sometimes it might be good to write down your thoughts like a diary, so that they become clearer in your mind. This will mean you will not have to be anxious in case you forget any details.

So many thoughts and memories
Alice thought through her story and she remembered good and difficult experiences. You too will have a mixture of memories. Try and recall some of your earliest and happiest experiences with your family. It might be at Christmas or on holiday. Can you remember birthdays you had together? What was your best present? Is there someone you could share this memory with? It is good to give thanks and be thankful even though you have experienced loss.

In families, we all find that there is someone, whether dad, mum, a brother or sister that we relate to best. Do not feel guilty about this – it does not mean you don't love your other relatives. Can you recall some of your fun times with the person who has died? Although you are sad when a relative or friend dies, it is still good to laugh and smile about the good times.

What's a crematorium?
When a person dies, their body is either buried in a cemetery or cremated in a crematorium. Alice's dad was cremated, which means the body in the coffin is burned in a furnace. This is at a very high temperature so that only ashes remain. Because the body is dead, there is no pain. The ashes can be placed in a box and buried in a special place like a church cemetery. Sometimes the box has a key, and the relatives can keep it. Other people prefer to scatter the ashes – perhaps at a favourite place that the deceased loved while they were alive. It might be in the countryside or at the seaside, for example.

It is good to go and visit the place where your relative was buried or where the ashes were placed. It gives you permission to stop and think about your memories. It is a time to talk with a friend or relative about your feelings. You may be like Alice and find yourself crying, but this is okay. There are times to cry, times to laugh and times to remember. This then allows you to get on with the rest of your life without feeling guilty.

Notes on Chapter 2

Remembering Great Days

Hearing bad news

Can you remember the time you discovered your relative was ill? Who told you, and how did you feel? Often we can feel numb when we first find out – that's our mind giving us time to take in the dreadful news gradually. Sometimes adults avoid telling young people the truth right away, or try to tell you only some of the facts. They do this in kindness because they find it very difficult to share bad news and want to protect you – they are also upset themselves and are trying to cope with their own feelings – but this can leave you feeling unsure of what is happening, and perhaps angry. Try and remember that parents are only doing their best to deal with a situation they have never been in before. Eventually, we need to forgive people who found it difficult to share sad news with us and understand that they have tried to help in their own way.

Hopes and fears

Often, we hope that the sick person will get better even though the doctor may have indicated otherwise. We all place hope in people and things. Alice asked God to help her dad. Whom did you place your hope in? Was it God, or a doctor or perhaps the sick person? Hope is something we all need – even if, as in this situation, it does not turn out as expected. It does not mean you cannot go on hoping in God, doctors or family.

When someone you care for is very ill, you might be uncertain about whether to visit them if they are in hospital. If you are able to face the situation and go and see them, it may help you accept the fact that they might die. Your relative or friend has not changed and still needs to know that you care for them. Even if they are asleep or in a coma, it can help to visit and talk to them, to tell them that they are special to you.

When your relative became ill, did it change your daily routine? Did it make you feel frustrated or annoyed? Try and remember that no one wants to be ill. There would be a change in lifestyle not just for you but all of your family. It is not uncommon, when a young person is worried, not to want to go to school. Adults can feel the same way about their work. We can either run away from our worries and hide at home or we can try and face them by keeping to a healthy routine. It is only natural to want to be near our loved ones when they are unwell, but we should remember that we do not want to make them more upset by causing them to worry about us. Why not let a teacher know what is happening at home? Then the school can support you and listen to some of your worries.

Can you think of any characteristic sayings your relatives use? It is good to remember them. At times the things parents say can irritate us but they can also make us laugh as we remember what makes them unique.

Notes on Chapter 3

A Strange Smell

Everybody worries about things that are important to them. In particular, we can feel anxious if we think a friend or relative is ill. Often we do not have all the information – and that can cause our imagination to run wild. This can also happen when we have actually lost someone we loved. It is important to talk to someone when we feel anxious. We all need someone to reassure us and help us understand the situation better.

Hospitals

Hospitals can seem strange places when you visit for the first time. They are like schools, with their corridors and special rooms. Because they have to be especially clean, hospitals can seem to have a smell all of their own. Remember that hospitals are full of people like doctors and nurses who only want to help and care for sick people, including your relatives. Older hospitals have long wards with up to ten or twenty patients all in the same room. However, newer hospitals have much smaller wards of four to six beds.

Hospitals are not very private places, so it is not always easy to talk. Young people can find it embarrassing having to see relatives or friends in a ward. Patients themselves do not find it easy, being in bed with other people watching. When we are nervous in a strange place, we can often do or say silly things. If you have found it difficult or have behaved in a way that upset others, then you are not alone. Do not judge yourself too harshly.

Arguments
Alice heard her parents argue when she was in her bedroom. Perhaps you too have heard or seen families having disagreements. They can leave you feeling upset and unsure about what will happen next. If you hear an argument at night while you are in bed, the noise seems to travel and sound very loud. All families have arguments at some time or other. People tend to get angry when they themselves feel hurt or are not coping very well with life. We often do not have all the facts about why people argue, so we should try not to judge either person. Remember that parents often say sorry and become friends again even though we do not see them do it. Although parents argue, especially at difficult and tense times, it does not stop you from loving both of them.

Notes on Chapter 4

Losing Weight

Alice's life changed in many ways when her dad became ill. There were things she used to do with him that he was now unable to cope with. New people began visiting their home, such as doctors and nurses. It even led to a change of bedroom for her dad. Change of any kind can often be difficult to adjust to. Our lives are changing all of the time. Some changes we look forward to, such as holidays and Christmas. At other times we can be negative about change. Going to a new school or moving house can make us feel anxious and unsure about the future.

So much change!
When someone in a family becomes ill, or dies, we naturally feel worried about the future. To help us cope, we can write down a list of the things that have changed in our lives. The list could be very long. It could include food, clothes, activities, sport, likes, dislikes, and people. It is surprising how much changes in our lives and how well we manage to cope and adjust. Be encouraged when you realise how well you have come through some of the changes in your life. Although the change you are now facing may be the biggest you have had, with support you can come through this time with a sense of achievement.

Remember that as a situation around you changes, and as people change because of illness in a home, you too are changing. You are having to think through lots of questions. What if my relative is ill for a long time? What if my relative dies? What if we have to move house? And so on. These questions are not easy to answer but by thinking about them you are preparing yourself to cope with what ever happens. Sometimes we cannot see any changes within ourselves. Why not ask someone close, whom you trust, whether they have noticed any change in you?

All these new visitors!
When someone is ill, or if they die, it can mean that strangers seem to arrive at your home. There is often an uncomfortable feeling when we meet people whom we do not know. We can feel embarrassed and perhaps, like Alice, would prefer that they did not call. However, the doctors and nurses can be very important to your relatives. They visit your home, bringing all their experience in caring for families just like yours. Remember that they can never replace the important role you play in loving your relative, and they will not try or even want to do so. Sometimes we have questions which the doctor or nurse could help to answer. It can be useful to write down what you want to ask.

Why won't people talk about it?
Often, parents try and shield their children from any difficult news. This is not because they do not trust you, but they are simply trying to protect you. If you want to know more information, then by writing it down you are showing how serious you are about the situation and how capable you are of hearing and talking about the issue.

Sometimes a parent knows that they are dying but chooses not to talk about it. We can feel left out as if they did not trust us. We need to remember that the person who is dying is having to cope with their illness as well as with how everyone else is coping with the situation. This is not easy for them. They may feel that they would get too upset by talking to you. It is not that they do not love you, or want to talk to you, it is simply too painful for them because they want to protect you.

Will I or someone else get ill, too?
When you spend time with someone who is ill, it is understandable that you yourself might wonder whether you will become ill, also. When a parent dies you can also be worried that your remaining parent might die. It is good to tell someone about your fears and worries. If you tell your mum or dad, they can reassure you. Your parents' doctor can also talk to you about your relative's illness and whether it would affect you and the rest of your family. Remember that it is always better to share with someone, instead of leaving your thoughts only in your head.

Will it help if I pray?
Alice prayed that her dad would get better. Prayer is a good way of letting your feelings and thoughts out. Prayer is more than just getting God to do what you want. It is a relationship in which you can share your life with God. As in any relationship, you do not always get what you want, but knowing that he is always willing to listen can be an encouragement to you. It is not uncommon for people to feel angry with God when life does not

turn out as expected. It is quite all right to feel angry with God. He understands, and shares our feelings – and he won't ever stop loving us, however angry we get.

Notes on Chapter 5

Never the Same

Every person reacts to bad news in their own way. You may feel numb inside, unable to speak. One person might keep bursting into tears and sobbing uncontrollably, while another might not be able to cry even if they want to. However you react, it will feel strange, but do not worry about it. You can react in what ever way you feel. You may think friends and relatives are acting strangely. This is because they just do not know what to say or do. People find themselves saying silly things and then feel embarrassed, but this is just a nervous reaction that will pass.

Could I have stopped it happening?
You may start thinking you could have done plenty of things to prevent the person you care about from dying, and blame yourself for failing to prevent the accident or protect them from the illness. Whatever happened, however the person you love died, *it is not your fault!*

At the same time as feeling guilty, you might feel very angry with the person and blame them for not being more careful, or not trying hard enough to get well. On top of everything, you still cling to the idea that the person is not dead, that it is really a mistake and any minute they will walk through the door.

Should I go and see them?
Seeing the body of a dead relative or friend can help you to accept that they are really dead. Your family may ask if you want to do this. You may visit a chapel of rest, which is like a small church, or the body may be in the hospital ward with the curtains drawn around it. There is nothing to be afraid of when you see a dead person. They are still the same, but their skin may look waxy and feel cold. The body's life force has gone and you will be looking at the shell left behind. It is okay to touch the person's hand or cheek to say goodbye. You may want to kiss them. You will still be able to hold onto your memories of when the person was alive.

I wasn't asked!
Sometimes young people are not asked whether they want to see their relative, and you may feel hurt by this. Adults are only trying to protect you from pain. If you do not get to see your relative or friend, and you wanted to, it helps to ask someone who did see the body to tell you how it looked.

Will there be a 'post-mortem'?
Sometimes, if the doctors are unsure why the person died, they may have to carry out a 'post-mortem' or 'autopsy'. This means they do tests and examine the body to find out the exact cause of the death. You may not want this to happen, but getting all the facts helps doctors to care for other people better in the future.

What's this about an organ donor card?
You might find out that your relative or friend carried a donor card. This card gives permission for a person's

organs to be used to help other people who are very ill to have a chance to get better. Sometimes it is not possible to use the organs, but you may have mixed feelings about it if they are used. Try and think positively about the way your relative or friend wanted to care for others. When the doctors are finished, you can still see the person to say goodbye, and they will still look the same.

Your mind will be constantly filled with thoughts about the dead person. This will be the same for the adults around you, and that makes it hard for them to think about you. You are still very important to them, and after a while they will have more space in their thoughts for you. In the first few days there will be lots of details to arrange. All the adults will be very busy, and there will be various visitors. A clergy person will call and, if you are up to it, you may join in with the discussion about the funeral and how you want your relative to be remembered.

What about the funeral?
If you have never been to a funeral before, you may wonder whether you would like to go. There is nothing to be afraid of. You simply have to be yourself. Some people find that their anxiety beforehand is far worse than the actual funeral. If you understand what will happen and are able to participate, going to the funeral should be a helpful experience.

Can I help?
Young people can help in planning a funeral. The funeral director will want to know what clothes your family would like to use to dress the person who has died, and you could help in picking a garment or a piece of jewellery.

You can help in choosing hymns and Bible readings, and poems or passages from books that were important to the person who died. If you know anything that your loved one liked, you could help your family by suggesting it. You and your family might like to write cards to attach to the flowers that rest on the coffin. The minister or a friend will talk for a few minutes about the person's life. When people are grieving they find it hard to think clearly, so if you can share a special story or memory with the speaker your help will be valuable and much appreciated.

What special things will happen?
It may help you if you visit the church a day or two beforehand so that you can be at ease within the building.

Different parts of the country, and different countries, have differing funeral traditions. In some places, but by no means all, the funeral director brings the body to the family home in an open coffin on the night before the funeral so that friends can come and visit, help to comfort the grieving family and pray in a special way. If this causes you any anxiety, then talk to a relative who will understand your feelings. In some families, they close the curtains in the house from the time the person dies until after the funeral.

There are no rules about what clothes to wear to a funeral. Some people wear black or dark colours to show that they are mourning the loss of someone special. Other people choose to wear something in bright colours because the person who died liked to see them wear it. So wear whatever you like, but remember that it is not help-ful to upset your family. It is much better to support your relatives than to argue about clothes.

On the day of the funeral, a family car will collect you and take you to church or to the crematorium. Sometimes the coffin is taken into the church first, but more often the family walks behind as the funeral directors carry it into church. Members of the family can carry the coffin themselves if they wish. Seats at the front of the church nearest to the coffin will be reserved for the family. During the service, feel free to react in a way that feels comfortable. You might want to cry, or you may find that all of your tears have dried up. Families usually ask people who come to the funeral either to fill in a card or sign a book placed at the back of the church. Sometimes the service will be recorded on a tape. This helps relatives who live too far away to come to the service, because they can listen to it later. It also helps the family afterwards because they may have been too upset to hear everything that was said in church. You might find that many years later you want to listen to the tape, look at the books and cards and think about happy memories of the person who died.

After the service, you may have to travel by car again to get to the cemetery or crematorium. The journey can be a tense time, because no one has anything to say. The second service only lasts a few minutes as the coffin is lowered into the ground or disappears behind a curtain to be turned into ashes. There may be a moment of silence when you have the chance to say a prayer of thanks for the life of the person you love, to ask forgiveness for anything you regret and to acknowledge that you will never forget the person who has died. Then everyone has the opportunity to look at the flowers and cards people have sent. You may like to take a flower and press it as a keepsake.

What happens afterwards?
If your relative is cremated, the ashes will be given to your family in a small cask or urn. Then your family will decide where to bury the ashes, or you may prefer to scatter them at a place that was special to the person you have lost.

Many people feel a sense of release after the ceremony is over. They want to share this release along with their memories. That is why families often have what seems like a party, with food and drink. Seeing your family and people you have probably never met before laughing and joking after the funeral may seem strange, but it is a good way of releasing fears and pressures. If you want some space to yourself, make sure you have a private room where you can go. Everyone deals with loss in their own way, and you must find a way that suits you.

Questions you might find it helpful to think about:
• What did you think about immediately after you heard the news?

• Do you think it was anyone's fault that the person died? Why?

• How did you decide whether or not to see the body of the person who died?

• Are you glad or sorry about your decision? Why?

• If nobody asked you whether you wanted to see the body, how do you feel about that, now?

• What contribution did you make to planning the funeral?

• Would you have liked to have done more – or less?

• What do you remember most about the funeral?

• What did you not like about the funeral?

Notes on Chapter 6

Friction

The days after a funeral can seem strange and hollow. Your relatives have to go back to work; you are expected to go back to school and get on with your work. It can seem as though the person you love and miss is suddenly forgotten. This may be difficult and upsetting, but it does help if you try to get back into a routine, even if you are not feeling like your old self. People around you, teachers and friends, find it hard to know what to say when someone's relative has died, so many of them choose to say nothing and this can hurt. It also hurts when people say silly things, like 'Try to forget about it.' But the chances are good that you will find someone who will listen to you when you feel like talking.

I don't want *to forget*
School might seem unimportant – irrelevant compared with the loss you feel. It will probably be hard to concentrate on lessons, because no matter how hard you try to stop it your mind will keep wandering onto thoughts of your dead relative or friend. You will probably find you think about them much more than you ever did when they were alive. Sometimes, people try to hold on to the person who died in their mind and in their heart, afraid that if they stop crying and thinking about their relative they will forget them forever. The fear is natural but there

is really no danger. You will not forget about the person you love.

I don't understand my feelings.
You will probably feel angry at the slightest of things, especially with your family. Do not be surprised at your anger – it is only natural to feel that way when something has happened to change your life completely. Do something physical, like P.E. or bike riding, dancing or taking the dog for a long walk. Do not worry if sometimes you feel like hiding under the bedclothes instead of getting up. Most bereaved people feel like this. It is important not to give in, but to share your feelings with your family, because they are probably feeling exactly the same. Sometimes, families rely on you to be strong and cope because it gives them courage to continue themselves. If you like, you can write down your feelings in a private diary each day; after a few months you will see how much progress you have made.

You might have recurring dreams about the person who died. You might enjoy this so much that you are disappointed when you wake up and the dream ends. People are usually glad to dream about the person they loved. Do not be afraid to share your dreams with your family, because they too will find comfort from your dreams. You will probably find that after a few months you do not have so many of them.

No one seems to understand
School might continue to be difficult for you for quite a while. This does not mean you should stop going, but get some help so that you can cope. If teachers do not under-

NOTES ON CHAPTER 6

stand how much pain you are feeling, they may misunderstand and treat you too harshly. Teachers will try and understand, but if they have no experience of grief, they simply will not know what it is like for you. You may not want to make a fuss, but it could help if a parent or relative spoke to the head teacher. Ask to be included in the conversation, if that's what you want. You will know in yourself if one teacher is more able than others to help you, so do not be shy about approaching that teacher. If there is truly no one at school, perhaps one of the youth leaders at the local church, or an older cousin, might be able to support you. You are the only person who can choose who to confide in.

So many questions!
You will probably find that you keep asking yourself questions that you never thought about before. These are difficult questions for adults as well as young people. If your family goes to church regularly, your own minister will help you to work through these questions. Even if you do not go to church very often, or at all, you still probably won't be able to stop asking yourself questions about God. Usually, when someone dies the local minister or a bereavement counsellor at the church may be able to help you work through some of these questions.

Where is my relative or friend now?
Christians believe that when a person dies the soul goes to God, leaving behind the body like an empty shell. God gives the person's soul a new, heavenly body or shell to wear for eternity. When Jesus was

dying on the cross, he said to one of the criminals crucified with him, 'I promise that today you will be in paradise with me.' (Luke 23:43)

When I die and go to be with God, will I recognise my relative or friend in their new body?
Yes, you will, because their soul will still be the same. That is what you will recognise. When Jesus rose from the dead, his disciples recognised him, even though he looked different.

What is heaven like?
We believe that heaven is a place free from the sadness, pain and death that exist in the world. We believe that God who made heaven also made the earth. When you look at several paintings by the same artist, you can see similarities in them that help you to know that the same person painted all of them. When we look at the earth that God created and see the sun, sea, plants and animals, in all their splendid colours, we know God's handiwork is good. We can conclude that heaven will also be a place filled with God's creativity – things we recognise and things we have never seen before. While we are on earth, God asks us to try to make it a better place to live, a little bit more like heaven. We can do this best in our loving, caring relationships with our family and friends.

Why didn't God stop my relative or friend from dying?
We do not fully know. When God made the world he said it was good. But he saw that something was missing – there were no relationships, so he created

families and communities. God does not want our relationships to be damaged, or broken by death. Because God loves and respects humanity, he also gave us freedom. Without freedom, all of life would be a prison. A child needs freedom to fall down while learning to walk. If your parent keeps you from falling by never letting go of your hand, you will never have the freedom or confidence to walk on your own – and you would be very irritated that they would not let go of your hand. God gives freedom to creation, and that means that things sometimes go wrong. And because all creation is inter-related, this affects every part of it. As a result, we are all affected positively and negatively by creation. Often the negative experiences occur through no fault of our own.

I thought God was powerful and caring.
The people who help us most when we are bereaved are the ones who listen and try to understand our pain and loss. God does this too, but not by being a genie out of a bottle who grants impossible wishes. Because Jesus died on the cross, God has experienced our pain and grief himself and knows our feelings. He showed his love for us by listening, and by providing people to support us. He gives us hope for our relatives and friends, and for ourselves.

Was it my fault that my relative died?
People often blame themselves when someone they care about dies. Perhaps you were angry or upset with the person just before they died. Maybe you

were busy at school or with friends and feel you should have been at home. When people die through illness or accident, usually there is nothing you could have done to prevent it. Your relative or friend would not want you to blame yourself. The life story of the person who died is unique and special. You can't see that person any more, but you can still hold onto their life story and remember special times together. *Your life is also special*, and the death of your relative or friend is an experience unique to you. It is one part of your life that will help you to learn new ways of thinking. God can help you to learn everything you can from the life of your relative or friend, and to use what they have taught you to make the most of your future. (If your relative was murdered or committed suicide, read the special sections at the end of these notes.)

Did God want the person I cared about to die?
The answer is no. God wants everyone to live long fruitful lives before they leave their mortal bodies to come to him. Because of the world's freedom, this doesn't always happen; and because God knows that we shall all die, he prepares a place in heaven for the person you love, like getting a room ready for a special guest. He also loves and comforts the people who are left behind and assures us that, as we believe in him, he will be with us all the time, whatever happens to us.

Questions to think about:
• When you went back to school, what did your teachers and friends say to you?

• What things annoyed you or made you feel angry?

• What dreams did you and your relatives have?

• What do these passages from the Bible mean to you?

John 3:16
This is how much God loved the world: God gave his son, Jesus, to live and die among us and rise into heaven, so that though we may all die, we can have life in his new world.

John 14:1-6
'Even though you are upset,' Jesus said, 'trust me. I have come from heaven and know that my Father has a place for you and your family. Heaven is like a big house with plenty of room. I'm going ahead of you to see that everything is just right for you. And when the time comes for you to join me, I will take you to my special house.'

Matthew 28:20
Jesus said, 'I will be with you as you believe in me. Day after day, night after night, I will be close to you.'

1 Corinthians 2:9
The Bible says that God has prepared for us a life so special that we can hardly imagine how good, exciting and special it will be.

1 Corinthians 15:20-28
All people die sooner or later. But when Jesus died he rose again and went to heaven. He has now made a way for us to follow him. Death is still painful, but Jesus gives us hope for our loved ones and ourselves.

1 Corinthians 15:35-46
When you sow a seed in the ground it appears to die. But we know that eventually a new plant is produced. It's the same when we die. God gives us a new life. This life is similar to life on earth but much better.

Psalm 23
Jesus is my friend. He is always with me. When I'm alone in my bedroom or outside with my friends, he gives me strength. He guides me through my ups and downs. Even when I am fed up and afraid he is encouraging me. He holds my hand and helps me to keep my balance. My friend prepares a party for me, with all of my other friends invited. I know he wants the best for me. His house will be my home for ever and ever.

Notes on Chapter 7

A Helping Hand

Alice's counsellor helped her to do a series of exercises which encouraged Alice to think about her loss. The following simple tasks could enable you to work through different aspects of your grief. You could perhaps choose to do one exercise each week. Doing it with another person, or showing someone afterwards, will give you a chance to talk through your thoughts and feelings. Why not keep them together in a special place which you can look at when you feel the need to?

1. Draw pictures of spring, summer, autumn and winter. With each picture, can you think of special times you have had in each season? Write them down under each picture. The seasons of life remind us that we are all on a journey which involves times of change. Change is a natural process that happens to all plants, animals and people. This tells us that although we may feel in a difficult 'winter' period, there will also be good times like spring and summer ahead of us in the future.

2. Hunt out photographs of yourself which show you at different ages. You may be able to do the same for the person who has died. This will help you to recall special times in your life and your family.

3. In your thoughts there will be both good and difficult memories. It is important that we remember the

experiences we have had of our relative or friend. Make a rainbow memory jar. You will need some ordinary salt, different coloured chalks, and a glass jar. Working on old newspaper, by rubbing one coloured piece of chalk over a small quantity of salt, you will change its colour. By doing this a number of times, you will end up with a range of differently coloured piles of salt. Think through your memory of your loved one. Link a special memory or period of time with a colour that seems to relate to it. Alice might have ended up with a jar like this.

You might choose to use a fancy jar or bottle. As you carefully pour the coloured salt into the glass, if you tip the bottle then you can also create angles which might express how you felt at the time. It might be helpful to do this exercise with another relative and to talk about why you each chose your colours.

4. On an A4 piece of paper, draw a big wave from the sea. At the peak of the wave, write a few words of how you feel on a good day. In the trough of the wave write how you feel on a bad and difficult day. It might look something like this:

5. You could draw a wave diary and express how you feel each day. In time, hopefully, you will see a change in how you feel and think.

6. Can you remember what happened on the funeral day? Would it help if you drew a picture of what you remember? It may be of the coffin in the church with flowers on the top, or at the cemetery with the grave stones all around you. Always remember to share your picture with someone so that you can tell them how you feel.

7. Can you draw on a piece of paper a jigsaw pattern with six to eight pieces? In each piece, write one thing about the illness your loved one had. It might be the name of the illness, the symptoms, how they felt, who helped them. You might feel you lack information about what to put. This could be a good time to ask someone like a relative or doctor to explain more fully what happened. Try and leave one piece of the jigsaw empty. This is important because we never know everything about a person or situation. We all have to learn to live with gaps in the things we know.

8. Go with a relative or friend to visit the grave or where the ashes were scattered or buried. You might like to take a helium balloon with you. In an open

space, you can think and pray any thoughts and wishes you have, before letting the balloon go and watching it float upwards to the skies.

9.   Alice wrote a letter to her dad as a way of asking questions and saying things that she wanted to but had never had the chance. You might find it helpful to do the same. You could either keep the letter or give it to your local church minister and ask him or her to pray for you.

10.   You could make two shopping lists. In the first, write down a list of your favourite foods you would like to buy. In the second list write down all the things you find yourself worrying about. Is there anything in the list which you could ask for help with? Is there anything you know your relatives worry about also? Find out whether your relatives worry about similar things. This will enable you to help each other.

11.   Finally, draw several large circles on a piece of paper. In each write the words IF ONLY . . . and then fill in some of your wishes. Are there any you know will not be fulfilled? Are there any you can do something about? Are there any wishes that you should share with another person? Think about one or two wishes that you can work towards so that you can achieve them eventually. Draw one final circle and leave it empty to remind you that you will one day wish new things that you can achieve.

Notes on Chapters 8 and 9

So Many Questions / Moving On

You won't be able to forget the birthday or anniversary of the death of your relative or friend, and you shouldn't try. It is much better to plan what you want to do at such times as a way of giving yourself an opportunity to remember and reflect. You could buy flowers, write a letter, or plant a shrub, or give a small gift to charity.

Christmas and holiday times are also difficult. Don't pretend that they are not, but spend some time talking about and remembering the person that you loved. By doing something positive, you are helping yourself to cope with your loss. Sometimes people buy a Christmas present for the deceased which then allows them to buy presents for the rest of the family. In that way at least you can feel you have not forgotten them. It may be just some flowers for the house or some new baubles for the Christmas tree. Exactly what you buy is less important than the fact that it allows you to continue your bond with your relative.

Gradually, over the months and years, you will find that you can do new things in your life and still hold on to positive memories of the person who died. This is exactly what they would have wanted you to do. By coming through your difficulties, making the most of your life, and growing up to be a loving and caring person, you will fulfil the desires of your relative or friend. As you have entrusted the person who died to God, you can also entrust yourself – your past and your future – to him.

Questions to think about:
- What happens in your family on the anniversary of your relative's death or birthday? What would you like to happen?
- How did you feel last Christmas?
- What new things have you learned about your relative since they have died?
- What new things have you achieved since then?
- How would the person who died feel about your achievements?

Special Notes on Murder

A murder is always a very big shock. If someone murders your mum or dad you will feel terribly angry with the murderer – and with your parent for allowing it to happen. You will have lots of questions going around in your head:

Why did it happen?

Why didn't the murderer kill someone else instead?

Why didn't my mum or dad escape?

Why didn't I realise and stop it from happening?

Why haven't the police caught the murderer?

Why is the court case taking so long?

Why are the newspapers and TV so interested?

It's my mum or dad, not theirs.

Did my mum or dad suffer?

I want to kill the person who did this!

When someone is murdered, they have no choice. They did not want to be murdered, and there was nothing they could do to prevent it. If your parent could not stop it, you have to accept that you could not have done anything either.

The police, newspapers and television are involved when someone is murdered and you may not like this. The police are doing their job, so try and let them get on with it. Your family will want them to find and punish the murderer. Most newspaper and TV reporters try to be considerate. You don't have to answer their questions.

You may want to take revenge yourself. This is a natural feeling, but don't allow it to eat you up inside. *You* are much more important than the murderer. Try to talk to someone about your need to take revenge. Maybe the best revenge is not letting the murderer influence you.

It takes a long time for a murder case to come to court – usually more than a year, and sometimes two or three years will pass before the trial. You have two tasks – try to understand in your own mind what happened, and then begin to adjust to not having your mum, dad or relative around any more. Even though what happened is awful, it can't take away all your good memories of your parent or relative.

When your whole family is upset, it is easy for them to try to protect you too much. They may not tell you what progress the police are making on the case, for fear of upsetting you, or they may not want you to go out anywhere on your own. Try and explain that you appreciate how much they care about you, but you need to know what's happening, and you need some independence. The first few months after a murder are a time when families often argue and get upset. Everyone is frustrated that they can't do anything to catch the killer, and at the same time they miss the person who died very much and find it hard to cope without them. It's hard, but try and forgive your family when they irritate you. The more you love them, the more you'll be helping the whole family.

Special Notes on Suicide

If one of your parents has committed suicide you will feel very hurt and confused. You may have all sorts of thoughts inside your head that you never mention to other people:

Why did Mum/Dad do this?
How did Mum/Dad feel when they did it?
Was Mum/Dad planning it for a long time?
Didn't they love me?
Was it my fault?
Why couldn't I stop them?
Why am I so angry?

All your thoughts and questions are sensible and you need to think through them. What you need is someone you trust who will listen and help you face these questions and find your own answers. Your parent or friend was no different from any other person. Everyone has periods in their life when they feel intensely miserable and then they may think about escaping their problems by killing themselves. For most people, this feeling quickly passes. You may even find that you are thinking about suicide. This is normal – most people feel the same after someone they love dies, and the best thing to do is talk to someone about your feelings.

Suicide is more common than most people realise. There are many reasons why people decide to kill themselves. One reason is because they have a mental illness and are unable to think clearly. Your parent or friend may love you deeply but their mind becomes trapped on a single thought. Like a racehorse wearing blinkers to keep it running straight ahead, all they can think about is suicide. This does not mean they don't love you. It just means they are preoccupied. When you are busy at school, or with friends, or watching television or a video, you don't think about your parents, yet you still love them. Your family might try to keep information about your parent's illness away from you because they think this will protect you. If this bothers you, talk to them about how important it is for you to understand. It might also help if you talked to your parent's doctor about their illness.

You may feel you should have helped your parent more, but remember that even experts can fail to recognise when someone is in need of help. Perhaps you worry that one day you will become so unhappy that you decide to do the same as your parent or friend. This seldom happens, especially if you can tell a friend or teacher about your fears and talk about them. You may worry about what to tell your friends when you go back to school. You may want your family to tell the teachers and pupils that your parent had a mental illness and died suddenly. This is the truth, but it also saves you from having to explain to everyone exactly what happened. But you may have a special friend or a teacher you can trust, and want to share your experience with them. You can learn from what has happened and use it to help yourself and to help others. Be sure to make a real effort to think about the good memories you have of your parent or friend. If this seems hard at first, it will get easier.

The Bible tells us not to take our own lives, and it also tells us that Jesus loves and cares for people who are ill. He forgives the mistakes people make and offers us the assurance that he will always love us. It may help if you say a prayer telling God that you forgive your mum or dad for what they have done and ask God to help them.